# Thru-the-Bible
# COLORING
# PAGES
## FOR AGES 2-4

**Standard**
**PUBLISHING**

CINCINNATI, OHIO

# THRU-THE-BIBLE
# COLORING PAGES
## FOR AGES 2–4

The Standard Publishing Company, Cincinnati, Ohio
A division of Standex International Corporation

© 1999 by The Standard Publishing Company
All rights reserved
Printed in the United States of America

Scriptures [marked ICB] quoted from the *International Children's Bible, New Century Version,* copyright ©1986,
1988 by Word Publishing, Dallas, Texas 75039. Used by permission.

Scripture quotations [marked NIV] are from the HOLY BIBLE—NEW INTERNATIONAL VERSION®,
copyright ©1973, 1978, 1984 by International Bible Society. Used by permission of Zondervan Publishing House.
All rights reserved. Printed in the U.S.A.

Scripture quotations marked KJV are from the King James Version.

Cover design: Brian Fowler
Coloring pages: Janet Skiles
Acquisitions editor: Ruth Frederick

06 05 04                                                    9 8 7 6

ISBN 0-7847-0970-X

# CONTENTS

| SCRIPTURE | TITLE | |
|---|---|---|

# INTRODUCTION

*Thru-the-Bible Coloring Pages for Ages 2–4* includes Bible story pictures, application pictures, and memory verse pictures that correlate to the most popular Bible lessons for young children.

A Bible story coloring page provides a quick and easy way to introduce a Bible story or help children review the story. Most of the application coloring pages feature modern-day children and will help young learners take the Bible lesson home. The memory verse coloring pages use simple and shortened verses that young children can easily remember and use.

Young children are still developing their fine motor skills. Their drawings are more like scribbles because they are experimenting with crayons on paper rather than working toward a finished piece. Many young children are not capable of coloring within the lines or filling in every space on the page. Encourage children to keep exploring as you help them have fun "coloring" and learning about Bible things.

Guided conversation is important in making any activity a Bible-learning activity. Use conversation about the coloring page the child is working on to focus the child's thoughts on retelling the Bible story, naming ways to follow the example in the picture, or remembering helpful Bible words.

While a simple coloring activity is fun for many young children, consider making it part of a more active learning experience. The following pages suggest ways to use coloring pages in age-appropriate learning activities for young children.

# BIBLE LEARNING ACTIVITIES
## WITH COLORING PAGES

### MORE THAN JUST CRAYONS

Fat crayons for the very youngest artist is a great choice. Also consider providing sidewalk chalk. To use finger paints, copy the coloring pages on coated paper so the paint won't absorb into the paper quickly and the child has time to be creative.

### TOUCH AND FEEL PICTURES

Copy the coloring page and mount each child's page on poster board or tagboard. Provide one or more of the following items for children to glue to their pictures: rice, beans, cotton, glitter, fabric, felt, popped popcorn.

### DRY RICE PICTURES

You will need 4 cups uncooked rice, food coloring (red, green, blue, yellow), plastic bags, wax paper, four bowls, poster board or tagboard, glue. Put five drops of food coloring in each bag. Add 1 cup of rice to each bag. Seal and shake the bag to coat the rice. Pour the dyed rice onto wax paper and allow it to dry. Put dried rice into bowls. Copy a coloring page for each child and mount each one on poster board or tagboard. Children glue the dyed rice to their coloring pages.

### CLASSROOM BIG BOOK

Use a large piece of poster board for each page of the book. Allow children to choose what kind of a book to make or provide each child a coloring page based on your teaching theme. Give children time to color their pages, then mount one page on each piece of poster board. Ask each child to dictate a sentence or two for her page in the book. Print the child's dictation under her picture and let her finish the page with a border, stickers, or fun designs. Put the big book together with three large rings. Have fun reading the book together.

### THEMATIC BULLETIN BOARD

Choose coloring pages based on a teaching theme. (See the index for Bible themes.) Let the children color the pages and add them to a bulletin board with an appropriate title. Consider cutting off the caption of the coloring page and allowing each child to dictate a sentence about his picture. Take pictures of your students and display each child's picture and name beside his coloring page. A bulletin board mounted low on the wall would be ideal for this activity.

## BIBLE LESSON VISUAL

Choose a coloring page that illustrates a story or application you want to teach. Enlarge the picture and enlist the help of older children to color it appropriately. Mount it and cover it with clear Con-Tact paper. Use the picture to introduce or review a story, or use the picture to talk about the lesson application. It will be sturdy enough for young children to hold and pass around the story circle.

## PERSONAL COLORING BOOKS

Choose coloring pages based on the theme you are teaching. Copy ten to fifteen different pages for each child. Make each child a personal coloring book: use staples, yarn, or folders to keep the pages together. Let the children take them home and encourage family coloring fun and Bible learning at home.

## MEMORY VERSE POSTER

Choose an appropriate Bible verse coloring page and make a copy for each child. Let each child color the verse page and then mount the page on construction paper. Adding borders of popped popcorn, stickers, rickrack, or fingerprints make the posters fun! Encourage children (and parents) to hang the poster in the child's room or play area.

"We love him" (1 John 4:19, KJV).

## PUZZLES

Copy, color, and mount on tagboard a coloring page that correlates to your teaching theme. Depending on the age of your students, cut the page into puzzle pieces (4–6 pieces for the youngest, 10–12 pieces for older children). Keep the pieces in a large Ziploc bag with an uncut coloring page. Many children will enjoy placing the pieces on the uncut page; others will want to work the puzzle without the uncut page.

## PLACE MATS

For special days and holidays, children can make place mats with coloring pages. Choose an appropriate picture to copy for each child. Pictures of creation work well for Thanksgiving, pictures of Jesus' birth certainly work for Christmas, and pictures of mothers or fathers with children work for Mother's Day and Father's Day. After children have colored their pages, mount each on a large sheet of construction paper, leaving room on one side for writing. Allow each child to dictate a sentence about the picture. Print the child's sentence on her construction paper. (Examples: We celebrate Christmas because Jesus was born. Thank you, God, for fruit. Thank you, God, for my mother.) Finish decorating the place mats, then cover them with clear Con-Tact paper.

## PRAYER TIME

Choose coloring pages that correlate to your teaching theme, or choose coloring pages that show a variety of things that show God's care. Display the pages and use them to focus the children's thoughts for prayer time. You might say: "This picture shows something that God made. Thank you, God, for fruit. Ethan, what would you like to thank God for this morning?" Or, "This picture shows a way that God cares for us. Megan, how does God care for you? Let's thank God right now."

## ACT IT OUT

Choose coloring pages that illustrate ways to help others. Display one page on each wall of the room. Travel with your children to the first wall. Talk about the picture, then ask everyone to act it out with a friend. Continue traveling around the room and acting out each picture.

## BEAN BAG GAME

Tape together four to eight coloring pages that correlate to stories the children have learned. Place the grouped pictures on the floor. Give each child a turn to throw a bean bag at one of the pages and tell something about that Bible story.

## CHRISTMAS ORNAMENT

Copy the coloring page of Baby Jesus for each child. Reduce as necessary to make sure the picture will fit on a margarine tub lid. Let the children color the picture and glue it to a margarine lid. Punch a hole in the lid and attach a gold cord. Put green or red construction paper or felt on the other side of the lid. Older children may want to add glitter around the edge of the ornament.

## MAIL IT HOME

For absentees or for a fun way to contact visitors, mail the coloring pages home with a note to the child. Children love to get mail, especially mail with a special activity to complete.

## MATCHING GAME

Choose a coloring page that correlates to the Bible lesson. Color one and leave one uncolored. Attach the uncolored page to one side of a file folder. On the other side, make a pocket large enough to hold cutouts from the colored page. Cut objects and people from the colored page and put them into the pocket. Children will have fun pulling out an object and matching it to the same object on the uncolored page.

# God Made Earth and Sky
*Genesis 1*

Thank you, God, for the earth.

## God Made Plants
*Genesis 1*

Thank you, God, for plants.

# God Made the Animals
*Genesis 1*

Thank you, God, for animals.

# God Made Wonderful Things to See
*Genesis 1*

Thank you, God, for things to see.

## God Made Wonderful Things to Feel
*Genesis 1*

Thank you, God, for things to feel.

## God Made Wonderful Things to Taste
*Genesis 1*

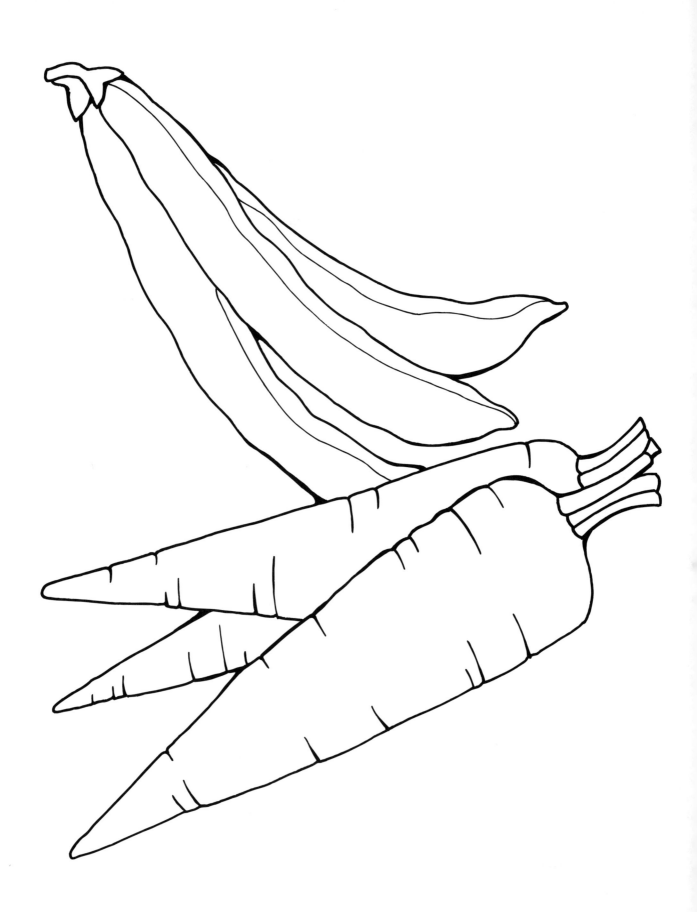

Thank you, God, for things to taste.

# God Made Wonderful Things to Smell
*Genesis 1*

Thank you, God, for things to smell.

# God Made Wonderful Things to Hear
*Genesis 1*

Thank you, God, for things to hear.

## God Made Adam and Eve
*Genesis 1, 2*

Thank you, God, for people.

## The First Family
*Genesis 2, 4*

Thank you, God, for my family.

## Noah's Ark
*Genesis 6–8*

God takes care of me wherever I live.

## Abraham's New Home
*Genesis 12*

God gives me a home.

Abraham and Lot
*Genesis 13*

Thank you, God, for my friends.

# Rebekah Helps Abraham's Servant
*Genesis 24*

I am learning to help at home.

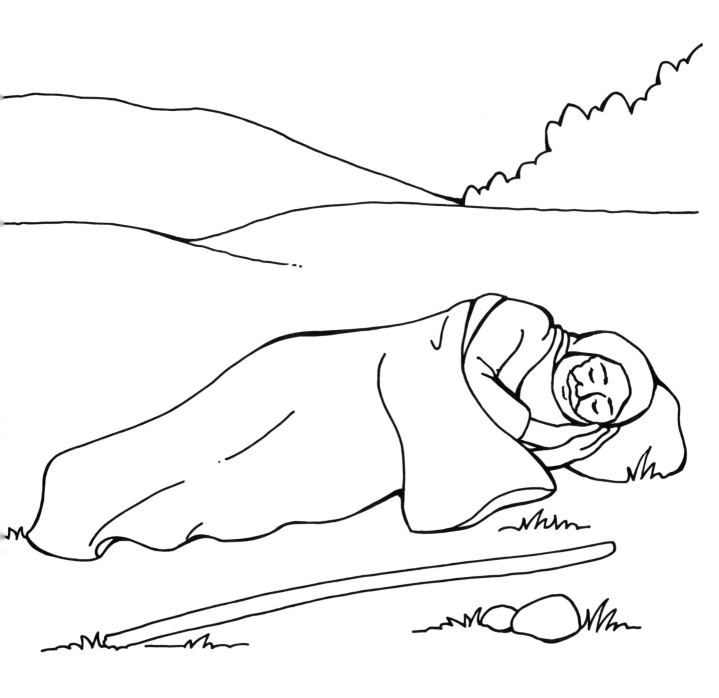

## Jacob's Dream
*Genesis 28*

God cares for me wherever I go.

# Joseph in Charge of Egypt

*Genesis 41*

I am learning to help.

# Miriam Takes Care of Moses
*Exodus 2*

My family loves me.

# Moses and the Burning Bush
*Exodus 3, 4*

Thank you, God, for my helpers.

# The Israelites Leave Egypt
*Exodus 6, 12, 13*

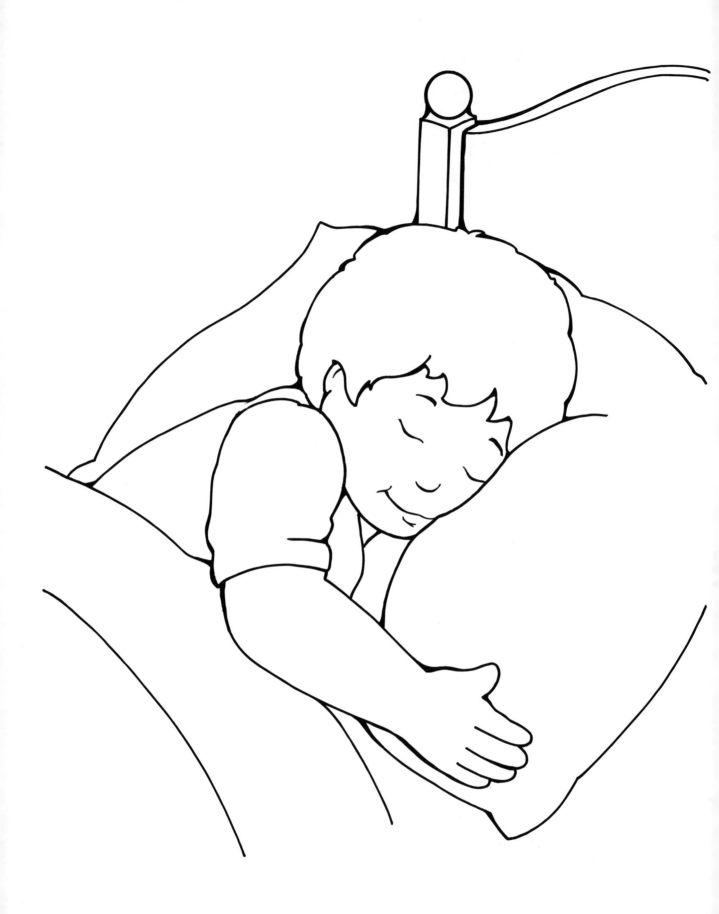

God cares for me all the time.

## Manna in the Desert
*Exodus 16*

God cares when I am hungry.

# God Gives His People Water

*Exodus 17*

God gives me water.

## Gifts for the Worship Tent
*Exodus 35, 39*

I am learning to share at church.

# Joshua Obeys God
*Joshua 1*

I obey God because I love him.

**Ruth Helps Her Family**
*Ruth 1, 2*

I can share with my family.

## Hannah and Samuel
*1 Samuel 1*

My mother loves me.

# Hannah Visits Samuel
*1 Samuel 2*

God gives me clothes.

## Samuel Helps Eli
*1 Samuel 1–3*

I am learning to help my teacher.

## Jesse and David
*1 Samuel 17*

My father loves me.

## David and Jonathan
*1 Samuel 18*

I am learning to share my things.

# David and Mephibosheth
*2 Samuel 9*

I am learning to help my friends.

## Solomon Prays to God
*1 Kings 3*

I can talk to God.

## God Feeds Elijah
*1 Kings 17*

God gives me food.

## Elijah and the Widow
*1 Kings 17*

I am learning to share with my friends.

Elisha and the Shunammite Woman
*2 Kings 4*

I am learning to share at home.

# Naaman Is Healed
*2 Kings 5*

God cares when I am sick.

## Josiah and the Scroll
*2 Kings 22, 23*

I read the Bible because I love God.

## Joash Repairs the Temple
*2 Chronicles 24*

I am learning to help at church.

# Hezekiah and the People Praise God
*2 Chronicles 29*

I sing to God because I love him.

## Nehemiah Helps Rebuild the Walls
*Nehemiah 2, 6*

I can help other people.

Ezra Reads About God

*Nehemiah 8*

I can learn about God.

## God Made Me With Feelings
*Psalm 23, 31, 56*

Thank you, God, for my feelings.

## God Made Me to Praise Him
*Psalm 43, 47, 147, 150*

Thank you, God, for making me.

## God Made Me Special
*Psalm 139*

Thank you, God, for my arms, legs, hands, and feet.

## God Made Me With Senses
*Psalm 139*

Thank you, God, for my five senses.

## Daniel Prays to God
*Daniel 6*

I talk to God because I love him.

## Gabriel Talks to Mary
*Luke 1*

Jesus' birth is happy news.

## Mary Praises God

*Luke 1*

I can praise God for Jesus.

## The Trip to Bethlehem
*Luke 2*

Jesus was born in Bethlehem.

# Jesus Is Born
*Luke 2*

Thank you, God, for Jesus.

## Angels Appear to Shepherds
*Luke 2*

The shepherds are happy. Jesus is born!

# Shepherds See Jesus

*Luke 2*

Thank you, God, for sending Jesus.

# Baby Jesus Goes to the Temple
*Luke 2*

Simeon and Anna knew Jesus was a special baby.

# Wise Men Follow a Star
*Matthew 2*

The star helped the wise men find Jesus.

## Wise Men Worship Jesus
*Matthew 2*

I can worship Jesus.

## Jesus Learns to Help
*Luke 2*

I am learning to help.

## Jesus Grows Up
*Luke 2*

I am growing up.

## Jesus Obeys Mary and Joseph
*Luke 2*

I can obey my parents.

Andrew Is a Helper
*John 1*

I can be a helper for Jesus.

## Nicodemus Talks to Jesus
*John 3*

I can talk to Jesus.

## Jesus Talks to a Samaritan Woman
*John 4*

I like to talk to my friends.

## Jesus Helps a Little Boy
*John 4*

Thank you, Jesus, for helping me when I am sick.

## Jesus Reads About God
*Luke 4*

I can learn about God.

# Four Fishermen Follow Jesus
*Matthew 4*

Jesus is my friend.

## Jesus Helps His Friends Catch Fish
*Luke 5*

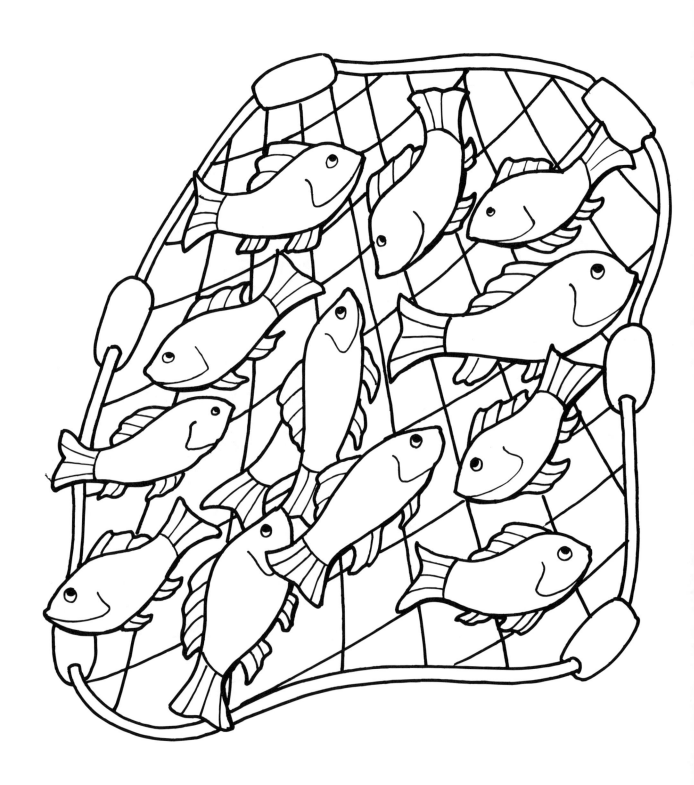

Jesus did many special things.

## Jesus Heals a Sick Woman
*Mark 1, Luke 4*

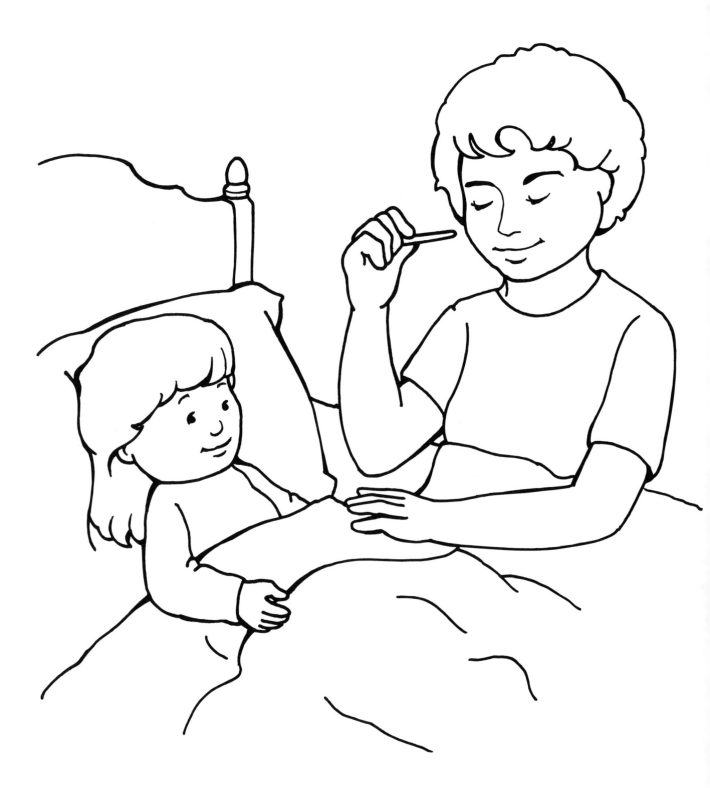

Thank you, Jesus, for people who care for me.

Jesus Makes a Sick Man Walk
*Mark 2*

Jesus did wonderful things.

## Jesus Calls Matthew
*Matthew 9*

Jesus is a special friend.

## Jesus Teaches His Followers
*Luke 6*

I am learning about Jesus, God's Son.

## Jesus Heals a Soldier's Servant
*Matthew 8*

Jesus made many people well.

## Jesus Quiets the Storm
*Luke 8*

God helps me when I am afraid.

## Jesus Feeds 5,000 People
*Mark 6, John 6*

Jesus used a little food to feed many people.

## Jesus Prays to God
*Matthew 14*

I can pray to God.

## Jesus Walks on Water
*Matthew 14*

Jesus is special. He can walk on water.

## Jesus Heals a Deaf Man
*Mark 7*

Jesus is special. He can heal deaf ears.

# The Man Who Said Thank-You
*Luke 17*

Thank you, God, for people who love me.

# The Good Samaritan
*Luke 10*

I can use my hands to help.

# Jesus Visits Mary and Martha
*Luke 10*

I can be a friend like Jesus.

# The Children Come to Jesus
*Mark 10*

Jesus loves me.

## The Lost Sheep
*Luke 15*

Thank you, God, for people who love me.

## Jesus Loves the Children
*Luke 18*

Jesus, thank you for loving me.

# Jesus Makes Two Blind Men See
*Matthew 20*

Jesus did special things to help people.

## Jesus Is a Friend to Zaccheus
*Luke 19*

Jesus is my special friend.

A Special Meal
*John 12*

Thank you, Jesus, for being my friend.

## Praising Jesus
*Mark 11*

I like to sing to Jesus.

## Children Praise Jesus

*Matthew 21*

Jesus, you are special!

## Jesus Enters Jerusalem
*Matthew 21*

Thank you, God, for Jesus.

## The Last Supper
*Luke 22*

Thank you, God, for Jesus.

## Jesus Is Alive
*John 18–21*

Thank you, God, that Jesus is alive.

## On the Road to Emmaus
*Luke 24*

I can talk to Jesus all the time.

## Breakfast With Jesus
*John 18–21*

Thank you, Jesus, for being special.

## Peter Helps a Lame Man
*Acts 3*

I can be a helper for Jesus.

# Barnabas Is a Helper
*Acts 4*

I can help by saying kind words.

## Philip and the Ethiopian

*Acts 8*

I want to learn about Jesus.

## Paul Begins to Tell About Jesus
*Acts 9*

I can tell about Jesus.

## Dorcas Helps Many People
*Acts 9*

I can help other people.

# Friends Pray for Peter in Prison
*Acts 12*

I can pray for leaders.

## Timothy Is a Helper

*Acts 16; 2 Timothy 1, 3*

I am learning how to be a helper.

## Paul and Silas Pray
*Acts 16*

I can pray when I need help.

## Paul Tells Lydia About Jesus

*Acts 16*

I can tell about Jesus.

## People in Berea Read the Bible
*Acts 17*

I can learn from the Bible.

## Paul on Malta
*Acts 28*

Friends help each other.

## Church Friends Send Help

*2 Corinthians 8; Romans 15*

I can help other people.

## Timothy Hears Bible Stories
*2 Timothy 1, 3*

I can learn about God.

# Philippian Christians Help Paul

*Philippians 4*

I can be a helper for Jesus.

"God created the sky and the earth" (Genesis 1:1, ICB).

"I will . . . help" (2 Samuel 10:11, KJV).

"God is good" (Psalm 73:1, ICB).

"God . . . made us" (Psalm 100:3, NIV).

"Love . . . God" (Mark 12:30, ICB).

"His name was . . . Jesus" (Luke 2:21, KJV).

"Jesus obeyed . . . his parents" (Luke 2:51, ICB).

"You are my friends" (John 15:14, ICB).

"Love each other" (John 15:17, ICB).

"Jesus is . . . the Son of God" (John 20:31, ICB).

"God . . . made the whole world" (Acts 17:24, ICB).

"We . . . are helpers" (2 Corinthians 1:24, KJV).

"We pray to God" (2 Corinthians 13:7, ICB).

"Be . . . kind" (Ephesians 4:32, KJV).

"We . . . thank God" (2 Thessalonians 1:3, KJV).

"He cares for you" (1 Peter 5:7, NIV).

"God is love" (1 John 4:8, ICB).

"God sent his son" (1 John 4:10, ICB).

"We love him" (1 John 4:19, KJV).

# INDEX

# CORRELATION TO STANDARD'S
# 2ˢ & 3ˢ CURRICULUM

The lesson titles for Standard Publishing's 2s & 3s Sunday school curriculum are listed below. The titles are grouped by quarters and listed in the order they appear in the teacher's book. In parentheses are the page numbers of the coloring pages that correlate to that lesson.

## AUTUMN, YEAR ONE
Wonderful Things to See (17, 18)
Wonderful Things to Feel (19, 20)
Wonderful Things to Taste (21, 22)
Wonderful Things to Smell (23, 24)
Wonderful Things to Hear (25, 26)
God Gives Us Families (29, 30)
God Gives Us Friends (35, 36)
God Gives Us Helpers (45, 46)
God's Care Wherever We Live (31, 32)
God's Care Wherever We Go (39, 40)
God's Care All the Time (47, 48)
God's Care for Our Needs (49, 50)
God's Care When We Are Sick (79, 80)

## WINTER, YEAR ONE
Happy News From God (101-104)
Born in a Stable (105-108)
The Shepherds See Jesus (109-112)
Gifts for Baby Jesus (115-118)
Jesus Grows Up (121, 122)
Jesus Helps a Little Boy (131, 132)
Jesus Heals a Sick Woman (139, 140)
Five Loaves and Two Fish (151, 152)
Jesus Heals a Deaf Man (157, 158)
A Friend for Zaccheus (173, 174)
Jesus Loves the Children (165, 166, 169, 170)
Jesus Hears the Children's Praise (179, 180)
A Special Meal (175, 176)

## SPRING, YEAR ONE
The Lost Sheep (167, 168)
The Man Who Said Thank-You (159, 160)
Jesus Is Thankful (183, 184)
Thank You, God, for Jesus (181, 182)
Breakfast With Jesus (189, 190)
Andrew Is a Helper (125, 156)
Friends Helping Friends (211, 212)
Paul Helps Lydia Learn About Jesus (207, 208)
Philippian Christians Help Paul (217, 218)
Arms, Legs, Hands, and Feet (95, 96)
My Five Senses (97, 98)
My Feelings (91, 92)
Made to Praise (93, 94)

## SUMMER, YEAR ONE
Ezra Reads About God (89, 90)
Jesus Reads About God (133, 134)
Timothy Hears Bible Stories (215, 216)
Philip's Friend Reads About Jesus (195, 196)
Church Friends Read the Bible (209, 210)
Jesus Talks to His Heavenly Father (153, 154)
A King Prays for Help (71, 72)
Friends Pray for Peter (201, 202)
Paul and Silas Pray (205, 206)
Nehemiah Helps Rebuild the Walls (87, 88)
A Lady Who Helped (199, 200)
Church Friends Send Help (213, 214)
Barnabas is a Helper (193, 194)

## AUTUMN, YEAR TWO

God Made Earth and Sky (11, 12)
God Made Plants (13, 14)
God Made the Animals (15, 16)
God Made Adam and Eve (27, 28)
My Mother Loves Me (59, 60)
My Father Loves Me (65, 66)
My Family Loves Me (43, 44)
My Friends Love Me (67, 68)
God Gives Us Food (73, 74)
God Gives Us Water (51, 52)
God Gives Us Clothes (61, 62)
God Gives Us Homes (33, 34)
God Gives Us Courage (149, 150)

## WINTER, YEAR TWO

An Angel Brings Happy News (101-104)
Jesus Is Born (105-108)
The Shepherds Go to Bethlehem (109-112)
Baby Jesus Goes to the Temple (113, 114)
Wise Men Worship God's Son (115-118)
Jesus Learns as He Grows (119, 120)
Jesus Obeys Mary and Joseph (123, 124)
Jesus Walks on Water (155, 156)
Jesus Helps His Friends Catch Fish (137, 138)
Jesus Heals a Soldier's Servant (147, 148)
Jesus Makes Two Blind Men See (171, 172)
Jesus Makes a Sick Man Walk (141, 142)
Jesus Teaches His Followers (145, 146)

## SPRING, YEAR TWO

Four Fishermen Follow Jesus (135, 136)
Jesus Visits His Friends (163, 164)
A New Friend (143, 144)
Jesus Is a Friend to Everyone (129, 130)
Talking to Jesus (127, 128)
The Children Come to Jesus (165, 166)
Praising Jesus (177, 178)
Jesus Is Alive! (185, 186)
Tell About Jesus (187, 188)
The Good Helper (161, 162)
Timothy Is a Helper (203, 204)
Peter Is Jesus' Helper (191, 192)
Paul Is Jesus' Helper (197, 198)

## SUMMER, YEAR TWO

We Read the Bible (81, 82)
We Talk to God (99, 100)
We Sing to God (85, 86)
We Obey God (55, 56)
Sharing at Home (77, 78)
Sharing With Friends (75, 76)
Sharing at Sunday School (53, 54)
Sharing With Family (57, 58)
Helping Each Other (41, 42)
Helping at Home (37, 38)
Helping Our Friends (69, 70)
Helping at Sunday School (63, 64)
Taking Care of Our Church (83, 84)